Say the sounds and blend them together to read the word: /r-ai-n/ – *rain*.

rain

Look at the letters and say the sounds. See how quickly you can say all of them.

Say the word *bee* and listen out for the sounds: *bee* – /b-ee/.
(There is one sound dot underneath the bee for each sound in the word.)

coats   tickets

Say the word *hat* and listen out for the sounds: *hat* – /h-a-t/.
(There is one sound dot underneath the hat for each sound in the word.)